MARVEL

AVENGERS ASSEMBLE

AGES
6-7
KEY STAGE 1

MARVEL

Times Tables

■SCHOLASTIC

Scholastic Children's Books,
Euston House,
24 Eversholt Street,
London NW1 1DB, UK

A division of Scholastic Ltd
London ~ New York ~ Toronto ~ Sydney ~ Auckland
Mexico City ~ New Delhi ~ Hong Kong

Published in the UK by Scholastic Ltd, 2016.

ISBN 978 1407 17171 5

Designed by Plum5 Limited
Printed in the UK by Bell and Bain Ltd, Glasgow

2 4 6 8 10 9 7 5 3 1

Papers used by Scholastic Children's Books are made from woods grown in sustainable forests.

www.scholastic.co.uk

Welcome to Avengers Assemble Times Tables!

Children learn best when they are having fun!

Avengers Assemble Times Tables is carefully levelled to present new challenges to developing learners. Designed to support the National Curriculum in England: Mathematics Programme of Study at Key Stage 1, this title offers children the opportunity to practise skills learned at school and to consolidate their learning in a relaxed home setting with parental support. With a range of activities and colourful stickers related to the Avengers, children will have fun learning and practising their times tables.

Avengers Assemble Times Tables will help children to develop two important numeracy skills. Firstly, being able to recall times tables facts quickly and effortlessly, and secondly, knowing how to use multiplication and division in practice. This book covers the 2, 5 and 10 times tables, as those are usually taught in Year 2.

If children can learn the times tables by heart, by all means encourage them to do so – a one-off investment in rote-learning will pay off for years. But it is important to understand that some children find memorisation harder than others and can become anxious or frustrated if they cannot remember an answer, which in turn makes recall more difficult. Patience and support – and breaking down the memorisation tasks into manageable chunks – are therefore key. Aim to achieve the correct answer before speeding up response time.

Throughout this book you will find 'Take a Break' pages containing fun activities for you to enjoy sharing with your child. It is advisable to keep sessions fun and short. Your child may wish to work independently on some of the activities or you may enjoy doing them together – either way is fine.

Have fun with the Avengers!

Developed in conjunction with Chris Andrew, educational consultant

Let's Practise Times Tables!

In this book you will find lots of activities to help you learn and use the 2, 5 and 10 times tables.

Learning your times tables is like gaining a maths superpower! It might seem boring but it's worth the effort because times tables come up in maths all the time. In this book you will find that times tables contain lots of patterns and that learning them can be fun.

- Find somewhere quiet to work.

- Work in short bursts, then test yourself to see what you can remember.

- Learn a times table thoroughly before going on to the next one.

If you are not sure what to do, ask a grown-up to help you read the instructions.

Check your answers on pages 44 to 46.

Don't worry if you make a mistake – everyone does when they're learning. Just cross it out and try again.

Let's Learn the 2 x Table

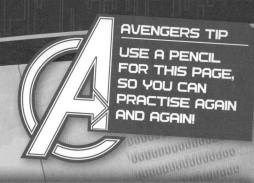
This is the 2 x table. It's **easy** to learn.

Just follow the five steps in the arrow as you fill in the 'You try' column.

1. **LOOK** – look at the sum
2. **SAY** – say it out loud
3. **COVER** – cover it with your hand or a piece of paper
4. **WRITE** – write the sum from memory
5. **CHECK** – check your answer

NOW FIND THE MATCHING STICKER!

The 2 x Table	You try...
1 x 2 = 2	
2 x 2 = 4	
3 x 2 = 6	
4 x 2 = 8	
5 x 2 = 10	
6 x 2 = 12	
7 x 2 = 14	
8 x 2 = 16	
9 x 2 = 18	
10 x 2 = 20	
11 x 2 = 22	
12 x 2 = 24	

Cover the table above and try these multiplication sums.

a. 7 x 2 = _____

b. 8 x 2 = _____

c. _____ x 2 = 12

d. _____ x 2 = 8

e. 9 x _____ = 18

f. 12 x _____ = 24

Finding patterns in a table can help you to **remember** it.

Look at the 2 x table. There will always be a 2, 4, 6, 8 or 0 in the units column.

The 2 x Table

1 x 2 = 2	7 x 2 = 14
2 x 2 = 4	8 x 2 = 16
3 x 2 = 6	9 x 2 = 18
4 x 2 = 8	10 x 2 = 20
5 x 2 = 10	11 x 2 = 22
6 x 2 = 12	12 x 2 = 24

So any number ending in those numbers is **ALWAYS** in the 2 x table.

This means that any number ending in 1, 3, 5, 7 and 9 **CANNOT** be in the 2 x table!

The answer to a multiplication sum is called a 'product'. For example, in the sum 3 x 2 = 6, **6 is the product of 3 x 2.**

Colour the numbers in this square that are the products of the 2 x table.
The first two have been done for you.

1	2	3	4	5
6	7	8	9	10
11	12	13	14	15
16	17	18	19	20
21	22	23	24	25

Let's Count in 2s

Ant-Man is leaping across the boulders, counting in 2s as he goes. Find the stickers to help him reach the last boulder.

2

8

14

20

Let's Complete a Table Wheel

Complete the 2 x table wheel by multiplying the number in each segment by the number in the centre, filling in the boxes as you go.
Two of the sums have been done for you.

Let's Play with 2s

Which weapon belongs to which Avenger?
You'll need to know your 2 x table to find out.

Draw a line to match each sum with the correct answer.
When you've finished, the Avengers will be ready to go!

| 7 x 2 | 9 x 2 | 4 x 2 | 10 x 2 | 3 x 2 | 5 x 2 |

| = 20 | = 6 | = 10 | = 18 | = 14 | = 8 |

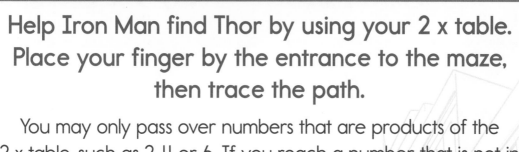

Help Iron Man find Thor by using your 2 x table. Place your finger by the entrance to the maze, then trace the path.

You may only pass over numbers that are products of the 2 x table, such as 2, 4 or 6. If you reach a number that is not in the 2 x table, you've gone the wrong way and must turn back.

Let's Divide by 2

Black Widow and Captain America are sharing out these weapons between them.

How many of each weapon they will get? Write your answers in the boxes.

a.

shields each

b.

hammers each

c.

arrows each

Superhero Sums

Can you do these sums using the 2 x table?

a. 5 x 2 =

b. 12 ÷ 2 =

c. 9 x 2 =

d. 3 x 2 =

e. 20 ÷ 2 =

f. 6 x 2 =

g. 12 x 2 =

h. 22 ÷ 2 =

i. 8 x 2 =

j. 10 ÷ 2 =

k. 4 ÷ 2 =

l. 7 x 2 =

m. 24 ÷ 2 =

NOW FIND THE MATCHING STICKER!

Take a Break

Use the numbers to help you colour in the characters.

= red

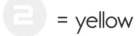
= yellow

AVENGERS TIP

USE THE COLOUR IMAGES AT THE BOTTOM OF THE PAGES TO HELP YOU IF YOU GET STUCK!

1 = purple

2 = green

3 = brown

Let's Learn the 10 x Table

This is the 10 x table. Follow the five steps again to help you learn it.

1. **LOOK** – look at the sum
2. **SAY** – say it out loud
3. **COVER** – cover it with your hand or a piece of paper
4. **WRITE** – write the sum from memory
5. **CHECK** – check your answer

The 10 x Table	You try...
1 x 10 = 10	
2 x 10 = 20	
3 x 10 = 30	
4 x 10 = 40	
5 x 10 = 50	
6 x 10 = 60	
7 x 10 = 70	
8 x 10 = 80	
9 x 10 = 90	
10 x 10 = 100	
11 x 10 = 110	
12 x 10 = 120	

NOW FIND THE MATCHING STICKER!

Cover the table above and try these multiplication sums.

a. 3 x 10 = _____

b. 4 x 10 = _____

c. _____ x 10 = 90

d. _____ x 10 = 70

e. 11 x _____ = 110

f. 8 x _____ = 80

Let's find a pattern in the 10 x table.

Look at the 10 x table. There will always be a 0 in the units column.

The 10 x Table

1 x 10 = 10	7 x 10 = 70
2 x 10 = 20	8 x 10 = 80
3 x 10 = 30	9 x 10 = 90
4 x 10 = 40	10 x 10 = 100
5 x 10 = 50	11 x 10 = 110
6 x 10 = 60	12 x 10 = 120

So any number ending in 0 is **ALWAYS** in the 10 x table.

This means that any number ending in anything other than 0 **CANNOT** be in the 10 x table!

Colour the numbers in this square that are the products of the 10 x table. The first one has been done for you.

Remember, a 'product' is the answer to a multiplication sum.

1	2	3	4	5	6	7	8	9	10
11	12	13	14	15	16	17	18	19	20
21	22	23	24	25	26	27	28	29	30
31	32	33	34	35	36	37	38	39	40
41	42	43	44	45	46	47	48	49	50
51	52	53	54	55	56	57	58	59	60
61	62	63	64	65	66	67	68	69	70
71	72	73	74	75	76	77	78	79	80
81	82	83	84	85	86	87	88	89	90
91	92	93	94	95	96	97	98	99	100

Let's Count in 10s

Hulk is thundering down the street, counting in 10s as he goes.

Find the stickers to complete his journey.

10

20

50

90

Hulk is leaping 10 metres each time he jumps.

Work out how many metres he has travelled if he jumps:

a. 3 times

b. 7 times

c. 5 times

d. 12 times

Look at the following sums and mark the ones that are right with a tick.
If any are wrong, Hulk will be cross so stick an angry sticker
next to those ones!

e. 1 x 10 = 10

f. 10 x 10 = 100

g. 6 x 10 = 16

h. 15 x 10 = 50

i. 9 x 10 = 90

j. 2 x 10 = 200

Let's Work with 10s

Fury needs to get to Iron Man.
Can you help him through the number maze?

He should only step on squares that have numbers from the 10 x table. Colour the squares to find the safe route.

14	33	18	91	45	88	8	120
51	88	41	11	22	38	15	110
96	29	53	8	4	90	100	55
3	64	12	36	70	80	21	27
16	48	40	24	60	17	56	32
6	30	72	50	93	51	5	78
9	20	24	19	2	82	1	13
10	98	39	7	56	99	61	49

START

Thor and Captain America are having a throwing competition.

Each time they hit the wall they score **10 points**. They each have two turns.
Count their scores and then decide who is the winner!

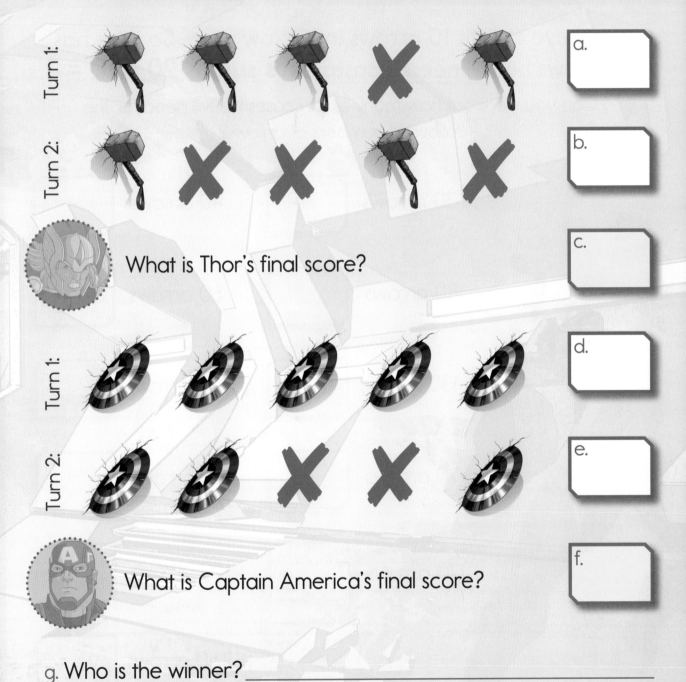

Turn 1:

Turn 2:

What is Thor's final score?

Turn 1:

Turn 2:

What is Captain America's final score?

a.

b.

c.

d.

e.

f.

g. Who is the winner? _____

Let's Divide by 10

AVENGERS TIP

TO DIVIDE A NUMBER ENDING IN 0 BY 10, JUST REMOVE THE FINAL 0!

Hawkeye can fit 10 arrows in 1 arrow case. So if he has 20 arrows he will need 2 cases. This sum is 20 ÷ 10 = 2.

Can you work out how many arrow cases he will need for the following numbers of arrows?

a. 30 arrows

b. 40 arrows

c. 80 arrows

d. 60 arrows

e. 130 arrows

f. 100 arrows

g. 70 arrows

h. 50 arrows

i. 170 arrows

j. 120 arrows

k. 160 arrows

Superhero Sums

Can you do these sums using the 10 x table?

NOW FIND THE MATCHING STICKER!

a. 100 ÷ 10 = [   ]

b.   2 x 10 = [   ]

c.   5 x 10 = [   ]

d.   60 ÷ 10 = [   ]

e.   10 x 10 = [   ]

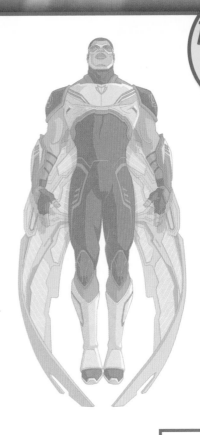

f.   40 ÷ 10 = [   ]   j.   8 x 10 = [   ]

g.   30 ÷ 10 = [   ]   k. 120 ÷ 10 = [   ]

h.   9 x 10 = [   ]   l.   50 ÷ 10 = [   ]

i.   4 x 10 = [   ]   m. 11 x 10 = [   ]

Take a Break

Find the words opposite in the word search below.

```
A N T M A N G I O A
M E J Z K U A R T L
J T P P I P X E Y R
I R O N M A N E G X
V E Y F A L C O N V
I R A M E R I C A H
S C A P T A I N O I
I N C P J H U L K L
O J Q T H O R C E V
N I C K F U R Y S O
```

AMERICA
ANT-MAN
CAPTAIN
FALCON
HULK
IRON MAN
NICK FURY
THOR
VISION

Let's Learn the 5 x Table

AVENGERS TIP
USE A PENCIL FOR THIS PAGE, SO YOU CAN PRACTISE AGAIN AND AGAIN!

This is the 5 x table. Follow the five steps again to help you learn it.

1. **LOOK** – look at the sum
2. **SAY** – say it out loud
3. **COVER** – cover it with your hand or a piece of paper
4. **WRITE** – write the sum from memory
5. **CHECK** – check your answer

The 5 x Table	You try...
1 x 5 = 5	
2 x 5 = 10	
3 x 5 = 15	
4 x 5 = 20	
5 x 5 = 25	
6 x 5 = 30	
7 x 5 = 35	
8 x 5 = 40	
9 x 5 = 45	
10 x 5 = 50	
11 x 5 = 55	
12 x 5 = 60	

NOW FIND THE MATCHING STICKER!

Cover the table above and try these multiplication sums.

a. 3 x 5 = _____

b. 2 x 5 = _____

c. _____ x 5 = 25

d. _____ x 5 = 55

e. 8 x _____ = 40

f. 7 x _____ = 35

Let's find a pattern in the 5 x table.

Look at the 5 x table. There will always be a 5 or a 0 in the units column. They follow this pattern: 5, 0, 5, 0.

The 5 x Table

$1 \times 5 = 5$ $7 \times 5 = 35$

$2 \times 5 = 10$ $8 \times 5 = 40$

$3 \times 5 = 15$ $9 \times 5 = 45$

$4 \times 5 = 20$ $10 \times 5 = 50$

$5 \times 5 = 25$ $11 \times 5 = 55$

$6 \times 5 = 30$ $12 \times 5 = 60$

So any number ending in a 5 or a 0 is **ALWAYS** in the 5 x table.

This means that any number ending in anything other than 5 or 0 **CANNOT** be in the 5 x table!

Colour the numbers in this square that are the products of the 5 x table. The first one has been done for you.

Remember, a 'product' is the answer to a multiplication sum.

1	2	3	4	5	6	7	8	9	10
11	12	13	14	15	16	17	18	19	20
21	22	23	24	25	26	27	28	29	30
31	32	33	34	35	36	37	38	39	40
41	42	43	44	45	46	47	48	49	50
51	52	53	54	55	56	57	58	59	60
61	62	63	64	65	66	67	68	69	70
71	72	73	74	75	76	77	78	79	80
81	82	83	84	85	86	87	88	89	90
91	92	93	94	95	96	97	98	99	100

Let's Count in 5s

Black Widow needs to climb to the top of the building but she must count in 5s to get there!

Add the stickers in the right order to help her reach the top.

60

50

30

10

5

Choose the correct answer for each sum. Colour the letter next to that answer.

a. 5 x 5 = 27? **H** OR = 25? **F**

b. 8 x 5 = 40? **A** OR = 50? **N**

c. 3 x 5 = 18? **G** OR = 15? **L**

d. 9 x 5 = 43? **R** OR = 45? **C**

e. 7 x 5 = 35? **O** OR = 30? **A**

f. 11 x 5 = 65? **P** OR = 55? **N**

The letters you have coloured spell the name of one of the Avengers.

Write the letters here to find out who: ___ ___ ___ ___ ___ ___

g. Iron Man and Captain America have **each** asked 5 Avengers to come and help them on their mission.
How many Avengers will come to their aid?

☐ x ☐ = ☐

h. Hawkeye has fired 5 arrows every day this week.
How many arrows has he fired in total?

☐ x ☐ = ☐

NOW FIND THE MATCHING STICKER!

Let's Tell the Time

Look at the small blue hand on the clock face below.

This hand shows us what hour o'clock it is. So this clock is saying it is 1:00.

Now look at the big red hand.

This hand shows us the minutes past the hour. It travels around the clock face once every hour. The clock is divided into 12 sections, and the red hand takes 5 minutes to travel from one section to the next.

12 x 5 = 60 minutes = 1 hour

Can you use your 5 x table to fill in the blanks, so you know how many minutes past the hour each section shows?

i.

j.

5

h.

10

g.

a.

f.

b.

e.

c.

d.

Can you work out the time on these clocks?

All the clocks are showing that the hour o'clock is **12:00**.

On the first clock the big red hand is pointing to the **2**, so the sum you need to do is **2 x 5 = 10**. The time is therefore **10 minutes past 12 o'clock**, which we can write as **12:10**.

12:10

a. **12:**

b. **12:**

c. **12:**

Let's Divide by 5

AVENGERS TIP

NUMBERS ENDING IN 5 AND 0 CAN BE DIVIDED BY 5.

Black Panther is trying to sneak into the warehouse but some of the windows are locked.

Windows with numbers that can be divided by 5 are unlocked. Can you circle them for him? Helpful hint – **there are 5!**

25

10

12

15

30

55

44

6

How many times will 5 go into your circled numbers above? Work out your answers below.

a. [   ] ÷ 5 = [   ]

b. [   ] ÷ 5 = [   ]

c. [   ] ÷ 5 = [   ]

d. [   ] ÷ 5 = [   ]

e. [   ] ÷ 5 = [   ]

Superhero Sums

Can you do these sums using the 5 x table.

a. 3 x 5 =

b. 10 ÷ 5 =

c. 5 x 5 =

d. 12 x 5 =

e. 30 ÷ 5 =

f. 1 x 5 =

g. 50 ÷ 5 =

h. 7 x 5 =

i. 25 ÷ 5 =

j. 4 x 5 =

k. 11 x 5 =

l. 40 ÷ 5 =

m. 9 x 5 =

NOW FIND THE MATCHING STICKER!

Take a Break

34

Can you be a superhero and find them all?

Let's Play with 2s, 5s and 10s

20	23	15	5	60
4	10	24	18	7
12	45	8	22	25
35	6	50		

AVENGERS TIP

LOOK AT THE ONES UNIT TO HELP WORK OUT WHICH TABLE THE NUMBERS ARE IN!

Doctor Octopus is hiding behind one of these doors. Thor, Iron Man and Falcon have to find him!

They know he is behind a door with a number in the 2, 5 or 10 times tables.

- **Thor** will search doors with numbers in the **2 x table**.
- **Iron Man** will search doors with numbers in the **5 x table**.
- **Falcon** will search doors with numbers in the **10 x table**.

a. Which doors will Thor open? _____

b. Which doors will Iron Man open? _____

c. Which doors will Falcon open? _____

d. Are there any doors which will be opened by more than one Avenger? If so, which?

_____

e. Are there any doors that won't be opened? If so, which?

_____

Let's Work Out the Sums

Look at the rows of hammers below. Can you count how many there are in each row? Now can you count how many rows there are?

You can multiply those numbers together to find out the total number of hammers.

There are 5 hammers in each row. There are 2 rows.

So the sum here is:

5 x **2** = **10**

Can you work out the following sums?

a. ☐ x ☐ = ☐

b. ☐ x ☐ = ☐

NOW FIND THE MATCHING STICKER!

c. ☐ x ☐ = ☐

Here Are All the Things I Can Do

PUT A STICKER NEXT TO EACH THING THAT YOU CAN DO.

I can remember...

The 2 x table

The 5 x table

The 10 x table

I can count in...

2s

5s

10s

I can...

Complete a multiplication wheel

Multiply numbers together

Divide numbers

Work confidently with mixed tables

Use my times tables to work out puzzles

Tell the time using my 5 x table

Calculate sums by counting rows of objects

More Activities to Share with Your Child

Find opportunities to use tables

Help your child to see that times tables really do turn up everywhere, so that learning them is worthwhile. Look for opportunities to introduce sums into everyday situations, for example:

- Sharing out toys between friends.

- Setting the table – if there are 2 pieces of cutlery for 4 people how many is that in total?

- Doing calculations that interest your child — if you are at school for 6 hours each day how many hours do you spend at school during 1 week, or during 5 weeks?

Make it fun!

Play games with the times tables.
For example:

- Recite the 5 x table while bouncing a ball, or marching up and down the stairs.

- Make two sets of cards, one with questions and the other with the answers, then match them up.

- Look online for websites that have interactive maths games.

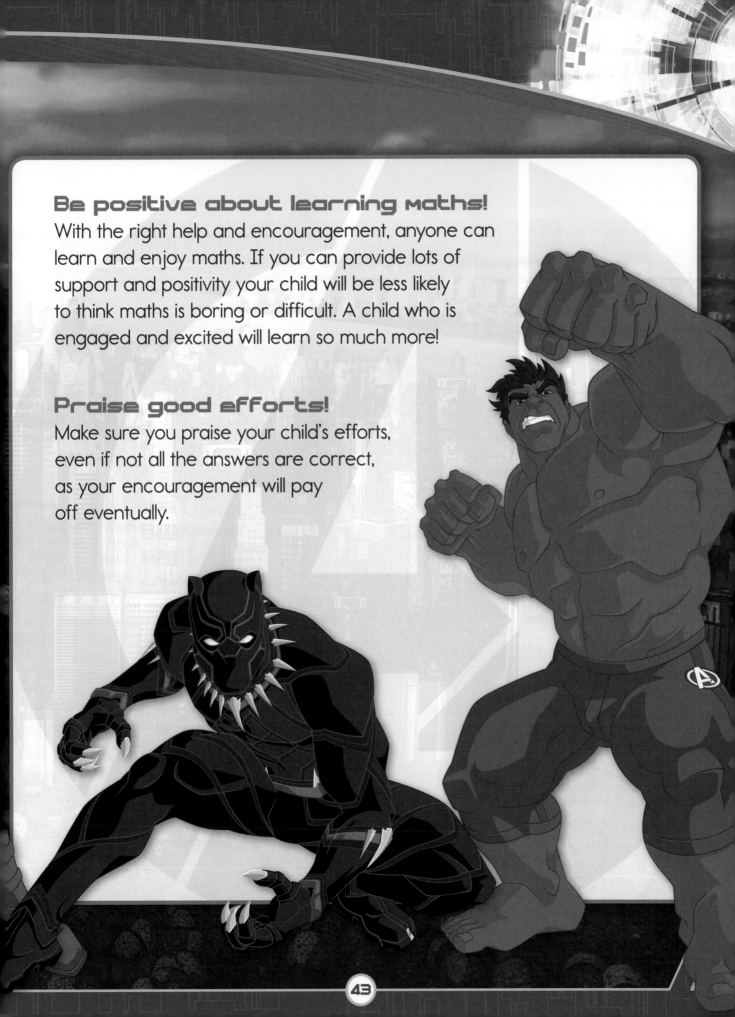

Be positive about learning maths!

With the right help and encouragement, anyone can learn and enjoy maths. If you can provide lots of support and positivity your child will be less likely to think maths is boring or difficult. A child who is engaged and excited will learn so much more!

Praise good efforts!

Make sure you praise your child's efforts, even if not all the answers are correct, as your encouragement will pay off eventually.

Answers

Page 6
a. 14, b. 16, c. 6, d. 4, e. 2, f. 2

Page 7

1	2	3	4	5
6	7	8	9	10
11	12	13	14	15
16	17	18	19	20
21	22	23	24	25

Page 8

Page 9

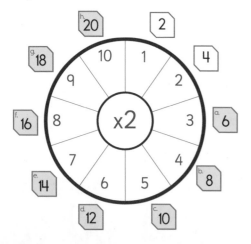

Page 10

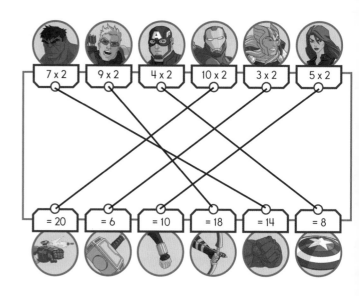

Page 11

Page 12
a. 5, b. 3, c. 10

Page 13
a. 10, b. 6, c. 18, d. 6, e. 10, f. 12, g. 24, h. 11, i. 16, j. 5, k. 2, l. 14, m. 12

Page 16
a. 30, b. 40, c. 9, d. 7, e. 10, f. 10

Page 17

1	2	3	4	5	6	7	8	9	10
11	12	13	14	15	16	17	18	19	20
21	22	23	24	25	26	27	28	29	30
31	32	33	34	35	36	37	38	39	40
41	42	43	44	45	46	47	48	49	50
51	52	53	54	55	56	57	58	59	60
61	62	63	64	65	66	67	68	69	70
71	72	73	74	75	76	77	78	79	80
81	82	83	84	85	86	87	88	89	90
91	92	93	94	95	96	97	98	99	100

Page 18

Page 19
a. 30, b. 70, c. 50, d. 120, e. right, f. right,
g. wrong, h. wrong, i. right, j. wrong

Page 20

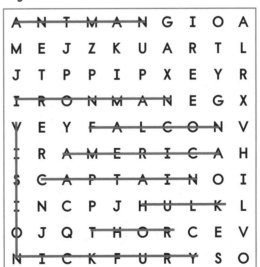

START · FINISH

14	33	18	91	45	88	8	120
51	88	41	11	22	38	15	110
96	29	53	8	4	90	100	55
3	64	12	36	70	80	21	27
16	48	40	24	60	17	56	32
6	30	72	50	93	51	5	78
9	20	24	19	2	82	1	13
10	98	39	7	56	99	61	49

Page 21
a. 40, b. 20, c. 60, d. 50, e. 30, f. 80,
g. Captain America is the winner!

Page 22
a. 3, b. 4, c. 8, d. 6, e. 13, f. 10, g. 7, h. 5, i. 17, j. 12, k. 16

Page 23
a. 10, b. 20, c. 50, d. 6, e. 100, f. 4, g. 3, h. 90, i. 40,
j. 80, k. 12, l. 5, m. 110

Page 24

```
A N T M A N G I O A
M E J Z K U A R T L
J T P P I P X E Y R
I R O N M A N E G X
Y E Y F A L C O N V
I R A M E R I C A H
S C A P T A I N O I
I N C P J H U L K L
O J Q T H O R C E V
N I C K F U R Y S O
```

Page 26
a. 15, b. 10, c. 5, d. 11, e. 5, f. 5

Page 27

1	2	3	4	5	6	7	8	9	10
11	12	13	14	15	16	17	18	19	20
21	22	23	24	25	26	27	28	29	30
31	32	33	34	35	36	37	38	39	40
41	42	43	44	45	46	47	48	49	50
51	52	53	54	55	56	57	58	59	60
61	62	63	64	65	66	67	68	69	70
71	72	73	74	75	76	77	78	79	80
81	82	83	84	85	86	87	88	89	90
91	92	93	94	95	96	97	98	99	100

Page 28

Page 29
a. 25, b. 40, c. 15, d. 45, e. 35, f. 55
The Avenger's name is FALCON,
g. 2 x 5 = 10, h. 5 x 7 = 35

Page 30

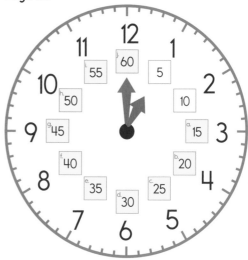

Page 31
a. 12:20, b. 12:35, c. 12:50

Page 32
25, 10, 15, 30, 55
a. 25 ÷ 5 = 5, b. 10 ÷ 5 = 2, c. 15 ÷ 5 = 3,
d. 30 ÷ 5 = 6, e. 55 ÷ 5 = 11

Page 33
a. 15, b. 2, c. 25, d. 60, e. 6, f. 5, g. 10, h. 35, i. 5, j. 20,
k. 55, l. 8, m. 45

Page 34
1. Iron Man's chest light has been filled in.
2. Captain America's shoulder badge is missing.
3. Captain America's shield has changed from red to green.
4. Thor's cloak has changed from red to blue.
5. Thor is missing a stud on his belt.
6. Hulk's trousers have changed from purple to red.

Page 37
a. 20, 60, 4, 10, 24, 18, 12, 8, 22, 6, 50
b. 20, 15, 5, 60, 10, 45, 25, 35, 50
c. 20, 60, 10, 50
d. 10, 20, 50, 60
e. 23, 7

Pages 38–39
a. 9 x 2 = 18, b. 10 x 3 = 30, c. 5 x 4 = 20

CONGRATULATIONS!

_____
(Name)

has completed the learning workbook:

Times Tables

Presented on

_____
(Date)

_____
(Parent's Signature)